Daisy D

Written by Rozanne Lanczak Williams
Created by Sue Lewis
Illustrated by Patty Briles

Creative Teaching Press

Daisy Dances
© 2002 Creative Teaching Press, Inc.
Written by Rozanne Lanczak Williams
Illustrated by Patty Briles
Project Manager: Sue Lewis
Project Director: Carolea Williams

Published in the United States of America by:
Creative Teaching Press, Inc.
P.O. Box 2723
Huntington Beach, CA 92647-0723

CTP 3218

Daisy likes to dance.

Dogs like to dance, too.

Daisy likes to dance.

Ducks like to dance, too.

Daisy likes to dance.

Dinosaurs like to dance, too.

Dance with Daisy!

Do the Daisy Dance!

Create your own book!

Make a list of words beginning with *d*. Draw and cut out a duck-shaped cover and pages for your book. Add wiggly eyes and a feather to the cover. Use the words from your list to write about other things Daisy likes to do.

Words in *Daisy Dances*

Initial Consonant: *d*	High-Frequency Words	Other
Daisy	to	likes
dances	with	too
dance	the	oops
ducks	like	oh
dogs	no	crunch
dinosaurs		
do		